WORKPLACE ROULETTE

GAMBLING WITH CANCER

DE MONTFORT

Published by: Windsor Occupational Health Information Service
&
Occupational Health Clinics for Ontario Workers (Windsor)
547 Victoria Avenue
Windsor, Ontario
N9A 4N1
April, 1996

Written by: Matthew Firth, James Brophy & Margaret Keith

ISBN   0-9680644-0-X

Printed and bound in Canada.

Windsor Occupational Health Information Service is a United Way member agency, staff are members of the Canadian Union of Public Employees (C.U.P.E.) Local 543.5

Cover Art & Design Layout by: Steve Tapajna

WORKPLACE ROULETTE

GAMBLING WITH CANCER

Matthew Firth
James Brophy
Margaret Keith

Windsor Occupational Health Information Service
&
Occupational Health Clinics for Ontario Workers
(Windsor)

April, 1996

CONTENTS

TABLES AND GRAPHS

ACKNOWLEDGEMENTS

To undertake a project such as this requires the encouragement of many individuals. We have had the good fortune to receive the assistance and support of many people from across Canada, the United States and England. They share our concern that workers bear a disproportionate and excessive cancer burden in relation to the rest of our society, which could be prevented if the political will is found.

We thank the following individuals for their assistance with this project: Carolyn Archer, Ken Bondy, George Botic, Niki Carlan, Judy Cook, Rick Coronado, Lissa Donner, Joe Divitt, Dr. Ethan Laukkanen, Dr. Michael Lax, Rory O'Neill, Bob Park, Dr. Abe Reinhartz, Homer Seguin, Greg Siwinski and Cathy Walker. We also acknowledge the following organizations/publications: Canadian Auto Workers (CAW), American United Auto Workers (UAW), Ontario Federation of Labour, Labour Institute in New York, Ontario Occupational Disease Panel (ODP), CAW Global Guardian, New Solutions, Workers' Health International Newsletter (WHIN), Windsor Regional Cancer Treatment Centre and the Essex County District Health Council.

We also acknowledge the special contributions of the Occupational Health Clinics for Ontario Workers (OHCOW) and the Windsor Occupational Health Information Service (WOHIS). The Boards of both of these organizations extended their financial and moral support to help bring this project to fruition.

We also thank the Centre for Occupational and Environmental Health at De Montfort University in Leicester, England and its director, Dr. Andrew Watterson.

Although we do not know their specific names and histories, we acknowledge the thousands of health and safety activists around the world who have given so much to protect workers' health against the dangers of diseases like cancer. It is their work that makes this undertaking so important.

The contributions of all these people and organizations were essential to the production of this book. To them we express our gratitude and appreciation.

FOREWORD

The idea to research and write a book about occupational cancer has been on our minds for a long time. For the past twenty years occupational cancer has been on the agenda of health and safety activists across Canada. This history has influenced us and shaped what we are presenting in this book.

In the early 1970s Northern Ontario hard rock miners - in particular Elliot Lake uranium miners - launched a major campaign to force the government to take action on high rates of lung cancer among miners. Their efforts compelled the Ontario government to sponsor a Royal Commission to investigate the miners' health problems. The Commission's conclusions created the framework for the enactment of Ontario's first comprehensive occupational health and safety law in 1978.

Trade union health and safety activists in Windsor began investigating carcinogens in the workplace in 1979 when the local press reported on cancer among Bendix brake assembly plant workers who had been exposed to asbestos for years without knowing the potential risks. This concern for potential cancer risks was probably the most significant factor in the formation of one of Canada's first community health and safety coalitions, the Windsor Occupational Safety and Health Council (WOSH).

To encourage and support workers' efforts to improve the work environment, WOSH co-sponsored, with the Canadian Union of Public Employees, the first labour sponsored health and safety awards in 1982. Colin Lambert, CUPE's National Health and Safety Director, suggested the awards be given in memory of Clifton Grant, a CUPE School Board carpenter who died at age 37 from asbestos-related cancer.

The recognition that many workers in a variety of jobs were at risk of developing cancer has remained an important issue over the last decade, as more and more workers have learned about potential occupational health hazards. In our community the majority of working people are employed in heavy industry. The production of automobiles and their component parts has produced not only cars, and pay cheques, but also increased rates of disease. In the mid 1980s autoworkers in Michigan and Ohio launched campaigns concerning increased cancer rates. The Ypsilanti General Motors workers convinced GM to hire Harvard University to examine the health effects of machining fluid exposure after discovering a cluster of brain cancer cases among workers in one department. The study involved over 46,000 Michigan GM employees and determined certain cancers were in excess of expected rates among workers.

The Canadian Auto Workers presented these findings to the Ontario Occupational Disease Panel (ODP) in 1993 and requested the ODP issue its own findings and recommendations to the Workers' Compensation Board. The ODP subsequently recommended that laryngeal cancer and machining fluids be added to Schedule 3 of the Workers' Compensation Act. Additional reports on other cancers are expected in 1996. The Ontario WCB has, for the first time, recognized a laryngeal cancer case related to machining fluid exposure. The case involved a Windsor auto worker who was exposed to cutting fluids for twenty years.

This book is a continuation of the process to build public awareness and support to prevent cancer. By 1999, the Ontario Ministry of Health anticipates a 50% increase in provincial cancer cases compared to 1990. In spite of this alarming trend, there is very little governmental action to curtail occupational carcinogens. The issue is summarized accurately by Dr. Peter Infante, the Director of the Office of Standards Review with the American Occupational Safety and Health Administration:

In the early 1900s, canaries were routinely taken down into the mines. The men used these canaries to give them the first sign of possible disaster or death. When the canaries passed out or died, the men knew that there was a problem with exposure to carbon monoxide and immediate action was needed. The analogy here is clear. Blue-collar workers appear to be the canaries in our society for identifying human chemical carcinogens in the general environment. (Today, their plight is even worse because we are paying little attention to their deaths.) The fact that occupational cancer is a sentinel for identifying carcinogenic exposures in the general environment is reason alone to justify an intensified cancer research effort in the workplace. Yet, our efforts to study their exposures to carcinogens, or to develop safe substitutes have been relatively minimal.

We believe this book is part of the greater effort to alert the public of the need to prevent cancer by eliminating carcinogens in the workplace and in the environment. Until workers' exposures are taken seriously, the general public will continue to share cancer risks as carcinogens accumulate in our air, water and soil.

Matthew Firth
James Brophy
Margaret Keith

April, 1996

1: WHAT IS CANCER?

1.1 CANCER IN THE WORKPLACE: AN INTRODUCTION

Despite millions of dollars spent on cancer research and prevention over the years cancer remains a serious health problem in Canada and around the world. At present more than 1 out of every 4 deaths in Canada is caused by cancer. [1] The prevalence of cancer deaths today is evident when present rates are compared to 1975, when approximately 1 in 5 deaths were caused by cancer and to 1900 when fewer than 1 in 25 deaths were caused by cancer. [2] In a recent World Health Organization study of 46 countries cancer rates for Canadian females ranked 12th highest, compared to Canadian males who ranked 21st highest. [3] In 1992 there were 115,000 new cases of cancer in Canada and 58,300 deaths caused by this horrible disease. [4] Only heart diseases claim more lives each year in Canada, but some researchers predict cancer, in the coming years, will surpass its rival and become the leading cause of death in Canada.

When these facts are considered the first question that comes to mind is: how is this possible? In a country where we pride ourselves on safe and healthy living and where some of the finest medical facilities in the world exist, it seems odd that cancer (an ancient disease) is an increasingly common modern concern. While the means to control other diseases (e.g. pneumonia, influenza, tuberculosis) are available, cancer is killing thousands of people every year.

The causes of cancer are at the centre of the issue. Recent estimates from a variety of sources have concluded 70-90% of all cancer cases and deaths are caused by environmental factors. [5] A person's occupation is one of the main environmental factors that may contribute to cancer.

3

1.2   CANCER AND OCCUPATION: A BRIEF HISTORY

Research into occupational cancer has been ongoing for over two-hundred years. The first report of cancer due to occupational exposure was documented in 1775 by Percivall Pott, a British surgeon, who described a high incidence of scrotal cancer among chimney sweeps who worked in filthy conditions. [6] Later others began to detect high rates of cancer as well. In 1822 J. A. Paris described excessive levels of cancer of the scrotum among Cornish smelters due to arsenic exposure. In 1879 W. Hesse and F. W. Haerting identified high rates of pulmonary cancer among metal miners. In 1895 L. Rehn reported an abnormal number of bladder cancer cases among workers who produced dyestuffs from coal tar. [6] And now, in the twentieth century, more and more reports are being issued each year that point to high rates of cancer in various occupations.

Not everyone agrees cancer and occupation are linked, however. Some employers and researchers deny that cancer can be caused by a person's occupation, despite evidence to the contrary. The ongoing controversy concerning the validity of occupational cancer is one of the major obstacles to eliminating cancer caused by the workplace. Sceptical researchers and employers must face the fact that occupational cancer is a reality. Only when there is a willingness to solve the problem will progress be made. Until such time, too little is being done and thousands of Canadian workers are at risk. The time for squabbling is clearly over. Occupational cancer must be addressed.

1.3 THE SHAMEFUL HISTORY OF ASBESTOS

Asbestos, commonly known as the Magic Mineral because of its indestructibility and fire resistance, is responsible for the premature death of thousands of workers from cancer and respiratory disease. In 1977 Dr. Irving Selikoff estimated that asbestos caused the death of 50,000 Americans per year from cancer and other diseases. [7] More recently, the London Hazards Centre Asbestos Handbook quotes Dr. Julian Peto who estimates that asbestos "now kills between 3,000 and 3,500 people in Britain every year and that this death rate will increase to between 5,000 and 10,000 in the first quarter of the 21st century". [8]

The dangers of asbestos related disease were known by the asbestos industry decades before the public was informed. Both Canadian and American insurance companies stopped selling life insurance policies to asbestos workers by 1918. Although the asbestos industry claimed not to know the extent of the hazard until after 1964, Johns-Manville quietly settled "out of court" in 1933 with 11 workers who had contracted asbestosis, an irreversible scarring of the lungs. [9]

In 1935, the first reports appeared linking asbestos and lung cancer. [10] That same year, senior officials of the two largest asbestos firms exchanged letters agreeing that "our interests are best served by having asbestosis receive the minimum of publicity". [11]

Canada opened the world's first asbestos mine in Thetford, Quebec in 1879. Unfortunately, the Quebec miners and textile workers were exposed to high levels of asbestos without warning or protection. In 1948, for example, Johns-Manville physicians x-rayed 708 workers at the Jeffery Mine and Mill in Quebec. The physicians discovered that only four workers had healthy lungs and then left without informing anyone of their findings.

In the 1970s Dr. Selikoff inspected the Johns-Manville plant in Scarborough, Ontario. He issued a serious warning about the dire health consequences for workers if asbestos exposures were not dramatically reduced. [2]

In the early 1980s the Ontario government called for a Royal Commission of asbestos to examine the extent of the health problems associated with asbestos exposure. This action followed after the scandal over cancer deaths at the Johns-Manville Scarborough plant became known to the public. CUPE school custodians in Toronto began exercising their right to refuse unsafe work after one of their members, 37 year old Clifton Grant, was diagnosed with mesothelioma. In Windsor in 1979, Bendix workers discovered the government had issued orders in the 1960s to protect against asbestos exposure but only informed the employer about these measures. The inspectors toured the facilities again four years later only to reissue the same set of orders which had previously been ignored. Unfortunately, for Tommy Dunn, a 34 year old worker diagnosed with mesothelioma, the company was still not in compliance with the 1966 orders in 1979.

The asbestos industry has used American bankruptcy laws to shield itself against asbestos exposed workers who developed cancer and respiratory disease. As we know from Dr. Selikoff's and Dr. Peto's findings, thousands more workers will die prematurely because of the asbestos industry's determination to keep workers uninformed about the true health effects of this deadly mineral.

1.4 TERMS TO KNOW:

CANCER: A general term for a large group of diseases characterized by uncontrolled growth and expansion of abnormal cells.

Normal cells grow by dividing, with one cell becoming two and two cells becoming four and so on. Genetic molecules (deoxyribonucleic acid or DNA) are copied when cells divide. DNA contains information concerning how the new cell will function and how it will divide. Healthy DNA also informs cells when to stop dividing. However, when cells don't stop dividing, they may keep growing until the host (the human body) is killed. This may happen when an individual develops cancer.

Contemporary medical theory asserts that a cancer tumour develops in stages, beginning with one cell. When a cell amasses genetic lesions (an injury or loss of function) cancer can develop. Genetic lesions can be inherited or result from exposure to carcinogens. Cancer is believed to develop when 4-10 lesions occur in a cell's DNA. As a result, most people are not destined to get cancer even though they may inherit cancer-causing genetic lesions. This view of cancer suggests that most cancers may be avoided by taking the necessary precautions. [12]

CARCINOGEN: Any substance that causes cancer when it comes into contact with animal or human cells by any route of exposure.

GENETIC CANCER: Cancer caused by hereditary pre-disposition to certain forms of cancer (e.g. some forms of cancer run in families). Also, a person's genetic predisposition may be reflected in some visible characteristics (e.g. people with red hair may be more susceptible to skin cancer).

ENVIRONMENTAL CANCER: Cancer caused by exposure to environmental carcinogens found in the air, water, soil and food. This group also includes lifestyle features (e.g. smoking, drinking and dietary habits), occupation and exposure to commercial products that may be carcinogenic.

OCCUPATIONAL CANCER: Cancer caused by carcinogens present in the workplace or encountered during time spent at work.

LATENCY: The period of time required for cancer to develop in an individual following exposure to a carcinogen. Cancer does not develop "over night". It may take many years for cancer to appear in a person after their first exposure to carcinogens.

How Much Cancer is Work-Related? The NIOSH Controversy

There is considerable controversy among public health professionals as to the amount of cancer caused by exposure at work. In 1978 scientists in the United States from the National Cancer Institute, the National Institute of Occupational Safety and Health (NIOSH) and the National Institute of Environmental Health Sciences estimated that 20-40% of all cancers were occupationally related. Industry reacted. The American Industrial Health Council (AIHC), an industry funded organization established to counter OSHA's plan to strengthen the regulation of occupational carcinogens, set out to disprove these figures. AIHC hired the University of Texas public health school professor Dr. R. Stallones to reevaluate the estimates. At the same time the US Centre for Disease Control released its own paper which stated "the United States was on the verge of an epidemic of occupational disease". (13)

9

2: WHAT CAUSES CANCER?

2.1 INTRODUCTION

Despite the popular myth, not everything causes cancer. The idea that everything causes cancer simply serves to complicate the illness and create a defeatist attitude that nothing can be done to prevent the disease.

Causes of cancer can be separated into two categories. The first is genetically caused cancer, which includes cancer caused by hereditary pre-disposition or other genetic traits. This group of cancer accounts for approximately 10-30% of all cancers. [5]

The second major classification of cancer causes are environmental factors. The main environmental factors are lifestyle features (e.g. tobacco use, alcohol use, dietary habits and sexual behaviour), as well as occupation, environmental pollutants, industrial products, sunlight and ultra-violet radiation and other factors.

A distinction is often made between lifestyle factors and other environmental factors because lifestyle factors are typically regarded within an individual's control; a matter of individual choice. The issue is not this simple, however. So-called individual choices are linked to other factors (e.g. socio-economic status) which influence diet, housing and other behaviours. It is narrow-minded to dismiss certain health hazards as being a consequence of individual choice and to conclude little can be done to prevent these hazards. In this light, social disparity, as an influence on lifestyle "choices", must be regarded as a factor in the environmental cancer equation.

Environmental factors are estimated to cause 70-90% of all cancers. [5] An important aspect of this statistic is that environmentally caused cancers can be more easily prevented than genetically caused cancers. This is simply because environmental factors (e.g. lifestyle features) can generally be more easily identified, controlled and eliminated. Because some substances are known or suspected to cause cancer, the next step is to remove these substances from circumstances where they put humans at risk (e.g. occupational use, environmental pollution). If environmental risks are controlled a large percentage of all cancers could be avoided.

In many cases, however, environmental factors combine forces to contribute to cancer. This process is referred to as the multifactorial cause of cancer. For example, a person who develops cancer who is also a heavy smoker, has poor dietary habits, works with carcinogens and lives in a heavily industrialized area, may be said to have cancer that is caused multifactorially. In such a case, it is difficult to determine which factor is the primary contributor to an individual's cancer. It is precisely this issue that is at the centre of the controversy surrounding occupational cancer because some employers and researchers attribute a person's cancer to more obvious factors (e.g. smoking), rather than to workplace exposures. This tendency shifts the responsibility for cancer away from the employer to the worker. While it is true many cancers are caused by several factors, this should not negate occupation as a significant contributor to cancer. A single factor (e.g. exposure to a carcinogen at work) may often be so significant, it may be the cause of the cancer.

2.2 SMOKING VERSUS OCCUPATION: THE CASE OF THE HARDROCK MINERS

In a recent report on lung cancer among hardrock miners, the Occupational Disease Panel (ODP) attempted to unravel the smoking versus occupation riddle. The ODP concluded smoking is the primary cause of lung cancer but also stated this should not eliminate the mining environment as a contributor to lung cancer. The ODP pointed to R. A. Kusiak's 1991 study, for example, where groups of gold and nickel miners with similar smoking habits were compared. Kusiak found the rates of lung cancer higher among gold miners and determined this excessive incidence of lung cancer had to be attributed to the mining environment and not to workers' smoking habits. [14] The ODP also cited the case of non-smoking uranium miners who experienced rates of lung cancer similar to the smoking general public.

As another example of how the work environment rather than workers' smoking may contribute to illness, the ODP examined cardiovascular disease among miners. Since deaths due to cardiovascular disease are often associated with smoking, high rates of death due to cardiovascular illness among smoking miners would be expected. [14] However, this was not the case. The rates of heart disease among miners were not higher despite their smoking habits which suggests smoking alone was not responsible for the illnesses suffered by miners. Therefore, the ODP concluded smoking and occupational exposure act together to increase rates of cancer among hardrock miners.

15

In another report Jack Siemiatycki compared studies which considered smoking as a confounding variable to those which did not consider smoking. His research concluded results do not vary meaningfully between studies that control for smoking and those that do not. [15] As a result, studies that focus only on occupation as a major contributor to cancer should not be dismissed as flawed or incomplete. In most cases controlling for smoking will not produce different results.

The case of the hardrock miners demonstrates occupation should often be viewed in the same light as smoking when it comes to assessing the causes of cancer. Ironically, while the hazards of smoking are well-known, occupational hazards are often not emphasized. This point was recently made by Dr. Peter Infante during a presentation to the U.S. President's Cancer Panel in October 1994:

With regard to cigarette smoking, there is a huge national effort to inform the public about the hazards and to reduce consumption. In contrast, there is little emphasis on the education of the public (including workers) about occupational carcinogens and very little emphasis has been placed on the reduction of these exposures. [16]

2.3 LUNG CANCER AND OCCUPATION

Similar evidence of elevated lung cancer rates due to occupation rather than smoking are documented by Joel Swartz and Samuel Epstein. The authors point out that lung cancer rates have been rising steadily throughout the twentieth century in most industrialized nations. While they acknowledge that smoking remains the primary cause of lung cancer, industrial causes (i.e. occupational and environmental exposures) in some cases contribute more to the risk for developing lung cancer than smoking. Widespread use of synthetic organic chemicals in the post World War II era in particular is a major reason why lung cancer rates have increased.

Swartz and Epstein list a number of examples where lung cancer rates among

16

workers exposed to carcinogens are significantly higher. For example: asbestos workers develop lung cancer at rates 8-16 times higher than the general population, coke plant workers in steel mills have an incidence of lung cancer ten times higher than other steelworkers, non-smoking uranium miners exposed to radon daughters have a rate of lung cancer ten times higher than non-smoking uranium miners who are not exposed to radon daughters. High rates of lung cancer have been detected among workers exposed to vinyl chloride, acrylonitrile, formaldehyde, epichlorohydrin, human-made mineral fibres, among persons working with chloroethers, and among workers in petrochemical refineries, copper smelting operations, tanneries, uranium, zinc and lead mines and among painters. [17]

A Second-Hand Carcinogen

Tobacco has been recognized as a cancer-causing agent for a long time. It is only recently, however, that second hand tobacco smoke has been identified as a carcinogen as well. A number of studies have linked second-hand smoke and lung cancer in particular. Recent Canadian estimates attribute 5.1% of male lung cancer deaths and 12.6% of female lung cancer deaths to exposure to second hand smoke from a spouse. The carcinogenic hazard of second hand tobacco smoke has lead many workplaces to ban or restrict smoking in the work environment.

Swartz and Epstein point out elevated rates of lung cancer have also been observed among populations living in the vicinity of industrial operations that emit carcinogens. In Contra Costa County in California, for example, lung cancer mortality rates in areas closest to a huge concentration of petrochemical plants are 30% higher compared to areas in the county with the least pollution and further from the petrochemical plants. [17]

Increases in lung cancer rates are clearly not exclusively due to smoking. Lung cancer is the leading cause of cancer death in Canada. In 1992 there were 15,700 deaths due to lung cancer, up from 14,200 in 1990, with 19,300 new cases of lung cancer in 1992, an increase of 2,000 new cases compared to 1990 and a fatality rate of 81% for lung cancer cases. [4] Industrially produced carcinogens that create exposure hazards for workers and contaminate the environment contribute significantly to increased levels of lung cancer.

2.4 IDENTIFYING CARCINOGENS

To determine whether a substance is carcinogenic three types of tests are generally used.

Bacteria Tests: With this type of test bacteria is treated with a chemical to see if its genetic material is changed by the chemical. If a change occurs the study concludes the chemical is carcinogenic.

18

Animal Tests: With animal tests a group of animals are exposed to a chemical over their lifetime. A second group of the same species is not exposed. A comparison is then made between the exposed and the unexposed group to assess the rate of cancer. If the exposed group has a higher rate of cancer than the unexposed group, the chemical tested is judged carcinogenic. Animals are used in tests because their cell structures are similar to humans. According to the International Agency for Research on Cancer (IARC), "all known human carcinogens that have been studied adequately in experimental animals have produced positive results in one or more animal species." [18]

Epidemiology: A great deal of what is known about cancer is based on epidemiology. Epidemiology is the study of the occurrence of disease (e.g. cancer) and other related health elements (e.g. carcinogens) among human populations. Unlike bacteria or animal tests which extrapolate information to human populations, epidemiology involves humans directly.

Epidemiology considers how often diseases occur, particularly among different groups of people. For example, an epidemiological study of can-

Common Sense Approach to Public Health

During the 1840s and 1850s thousands of people in London, England were dying from cholera. Medical science had no idea of the cause. The leading members of the medical establishment believed that it was caused by bad air.

Dr. John Snow, a young British physician who was treating cholera patients noted the disease was not spread from family member to family member. After 500 people died within a ten day period Dr. Snow observed that nearly all the deaths had taken place within a short distance of the much frequented Broad Street drinking water pump. Dr. Snow argued with city authorities and finally the pump was removed. New cases dropped dramatically. Although Dr. Snow never learned the actual cause of the disease a solution had been found. Dr. Philip Landrigan summarized,"*The principal lesson to be learned from Dr. Snow's work is that full and complete risk assessment is not essential to establish effective regulations that efficiently reduce diseases. Dr. Snow analyzed a pattern of illness, then drew reasonable conclusions and, on the basis of that interpretation, he removed the handle of the Broad St. pump. He prevented disease and he saved lives. Through his work he became one of medicine's heroes. Snow's work illustrates the axiom that full knowledge of causation is not a necessary prerequisite to the prevention of illness.*"(19)

Women Excluded

Cancer is a disease that can strike anyone. Epidemiological research, however, has largely excluded women. A recent study by Zahm et. al of occupational biomedical journals determined that of the 1,223 articles considered, 46% were limited to studies of white men, only 35% of the total included white women, with only 14% having any analysis of white women specifically, and only 2% had any analysis of non-white women. Zahm et al also observed that those studies that did include women tended to have weaker methodologies and were less able to produce significant data on the occupational cancer risks for women and minorities. These results are particularly troubling considering that 45% of all working people in Canada in 1994 were women and that women are increasingly entering traditional male occupations (e.g. mining, steelworking) where there may be potential exposure to carcinogens. (21)

cer may involve examining cancer rates for a group of workers in a plant. The cancer rates in this group may then be compared to another population (e.g. workers in another plant or the general population) to determine if an excessive level of cancer exists in the plant. This type of study is called occupational epidemiology and is based on analysis of workers'experiences. Information is collected to understand how diseases are caused by occupational exposures. The goal of occupational epidemiology is to prevent disease among working populations.

An epidemiological study may be conducted in a workplace in response to workers' concerns. For example, if workers in a plant are suffering from a symptom while using a particular agent or performing a particular task, this may encourage an epidemiological study which may then uncover an unsafe substance or practice that is responsible for the workers' ill-health. In this instance, steps should be taken to eliminate the risk to the workers involved. In many cases medical science knows what it does about a disease as a result of occupational epidemiology. This is the case with cancer, where the majority of known human carcinogens have been identified following epidemiological studies with groups of workers. [20]

2.5   CLASSIFYING CARCINOGENS

One of the most straightforward methods for classifying carcinogens is contained in the IARC monographs which rank carcinogens in four major classifications. IARC is just one of many agencies in the world that assess carcinogens. At this time, IARC has evaluated 775 substances and processes. It is estimated that humans are exposed to between 60,00-100,000 substances and less than 1% of these have been fully evaluated for their toxicity to humans. The IARC carcinogen classifications are as follows. [22]

Group 1 Carcinogen: There is sufficient evidence to identify the substance as carcinogenic in humans. In some exceptional cases a substance may be placed in group one when there is less than sufficient evidence of carcinogenicity in humans but sufficient evidence from animal experiments. IARC has confirmed 65 substances and practices are group 1 carcinogens.

Group 2 Carcinogen: This category includes substances which range from almost sufficient evidence of carcinogenicity among

21

humans to no human evidence of carcinogenicity but existing evidence of carcinogenicity from animal experiments. As such, this category is subdivided into Group 2A (substances probably carcinogenic to humans) and Group 2B (substances possibly carcinogenic to humans) based on the level and source of support for carcinogenicity. IARC has confirmed 57 Group 2A carcinogens and 205 Group 2B carcinogens.

Group 3 Carcinogen: This group includes substances that are not as yet classifiable as to their carcinogenicity in humans due to a lack of evidence of carcinogenicity from epidemiological studies and animal experiments. In some cases there may be evidence of carcinogenicity in animals due to a certain mechanism, however, this mechanism does not apply to humans.

Group 4 Carcinogen: This group includes substances that are probably not carcinogenic in humans. Evidence from both human and animal studies has demonstrated a lack of carcinogenicity.

The following lists from the most recent IARC evaluations [23] are some of the carcinogenic substances common to occupations. This list is not complete. If there is a substance or a process in your workplace that you suspect is a carcinogen and it does not appear in these lists, consult a more thorough source to ensure you are not at risk.

SELECTED EXAMPLES OF CARCINOGENS

Selected Group 1 (Definite carcinogens in humans):

Agents & Groups of Agents:

Aflatoxins, 4-Aminobiphenyl, Arsenic & certain arsenic compounds, Asbestos,

Non-Chemical Carcinogens

Chemicals are not the only cause of cancer. Exposure to electro-magnetic fields (EMFs) and ultra-violet radiation (UV) may also cause cancer. EMF sources include: power lines, wiring in workplaces/homes, household appliances and work equipment (e.g. computer monitors). Elevated rates of leukaemia and brain cancer have been reported in studies involving a variety of electrical occupations (e.g. utility workers, cable splicers). Ultra violet radiation from the sun is a widely accepted cause of skin cancer. Occupations that require outdoor work (e.g. farmers, construction workers, letter carriers, etc.) are at risk of developing skin cancer due to prolonged UV exposure.

Azathioprine, Benzene, Benzidine, Cadmium & cadmium compounds, Chlorambucil, Chromium (VI) compounds, Cyclophosphamide, Diethystilboestrol, Erionite, Ethylene oxide, Melphalan, Mustard gas, 2-Naphthylamine, Nickel compounds, Oestrogen replacement therapy, Oestrogens (nonsteroidal), Oestrogens (steroidal), Radon, Solar radiation, Talc containing asbestiform fibres, Treosulfan, Vinyl chloride.

Mixtures:

Alcoholic beverages, Analgesic mixtures containing phenacetin, Betel quid with tobacco, Coal-tar pitches, Coal-tars, Mineral oils (untreated and mildly treated), Salted fish (Chinese-style), Shale oils, Soots, Tobacco products (smokeless), Tobacco smoke, Wood dust.

Exposure Circumstances:

Aluminum production, Auramine (manufacture of), Boot and shoe manufacture and repair, Coal gasification, Coke production, Furniture and cabinet making, Haematite mining (underground with exposure to radon), Iron and steel founding, Isopropanol manufacture (strong-acid process), Magenta (manufacture of), Painter (occupational exposure as a), Rubber industry, Strong-inorganic-acid mists containing sulfuric acid (occupational exposure to).

Selected Group 2A (Probably carcinogenic in humans):

Agents & Groups of Agents:

Acrylamide, Acrylontrile, Adriamycin, Androgenic (anabolic) steroids, Azacitidine, Benzidine-based dyes, Bischloroethyl nitrosourea, Captafol, Chlorozotocin, Cisplatin, Diethyl sulfate, Dimethyl sulfate, Epichlorohydrin, Ethylene dibromide, Formaldehyde, 5-Methoxypsoralen, N-methyl N-nitrosourea, Nitrogen mustard, N-Nitrosodiethylamine, N-Nitrosodimethylamine, Phenacetin, Procarbazine hydrochloride, Silica (crystalline), Styrene-7 (8-oxide), Tetrachloroethylene, Trichloroethylene, Ultraviolet radiation, Vinyl bromide, Vinyl fluoride.

Mixtures:

Creosotes, Diesel engine exhaust, Hot mate, Non-arsenical insecticides (occupational exposures in spraying and application of), Polychlorinated biphenyls.

Exposure Circumstances:

Art glass, glass containers and pressed ware (manufacture of), Hairdresser or barber (occupational exposure as a), Petroleum refining (occupational exposures in), Sunlamps and sunbeds (use of).

Selected Group 2B (Possibly carcinogenic in humans):

Agents & Groups of Agents:

Acetaldehyde, Acetamide, Aflatoxin M1, Amitrole, Aramite, Auramine, Benzofuran, Benzyl violet 4B, Bracken fern, Caffeic acid, Carbon tetrachloride, Ceramic fibres, Chloroform, Chlorophenols, Citrus Red No. 2, Dacarbazine, DDT, 1,2-Dibromo-3-chloropropane, Dihydrosafrole, Ethyl acrylate, Furan, Glasswool, Glycidaldehyde, Hexachlorobenzene, Hydrazine, Isoprene, Lead and lead compounds (inorganic), Magenta (containing CI Basic Red 9), Methylazoxymethanol acetate, Methylmercury compounds, Mirex, Nickel (metallic), 2-Nitrofluorene, Nitrogen mustard N-oxide, Ochratoxin A, Oil Orange SS, Phenobarbitol, Potassium bromate, Propylene oxide, Saccharin, Slagwool, Styrene, Sulfallate, Thioacetamide, Toluene diisocyanates, Trypan blue, Urethane, Vinyl acetate.

Mixtures:

Bitumens (extracts of steam-refined and air-refined), Coffee (urinary bladder), Diesel fuel (marine), Engine exhaust (gasoline), Fuel oils (residual heavy), Gasoline, Polybrominated biphenyls, Toxaphene (polychlorinated camphenes), Toxins derived from Fusarium moniliforme, Welding fumes.

Exposure circumstances:

Carpentry and joinery, Dry cleaning (occupational exposure in), Textile manufacturing industry (work in).

2.6   HOW SAFE IS "SAFE EXPOSURE"?

Usually lists of carcinogens are presented with Threshold Limit Values (TLVs). TLVs refer to concentrations of substances in the air and list levels at which it is believed nearly all workers may be exposed to a substance without adverse effect, even with day to day use. TLVs typically measure supposed safe levels of exposure in parts per million (ppm) or milligrams per cubic metre (mg/m3).

There are many problems with TLVs however. First of all TLVs are established on the basis of "average" healthy male workers and are therefore exclusionary. TLVs do not consider the diversity of the workforce. Factors such as age, gender, health status and external exposures are not considered when TLVs are set. As a result, TLVs often over estimate safe exposure levels. For example, a pregnant worker, with a history of respiratory illness, may be more sensitive to a substance than the typical male worker who is in good health. In this case the pregnant worker may be at risk at levels well below the suggested TLV. TLVs also do not estimate the combined effects of different substances.

Research conducted by Castleman and Ziem has indicated TLVs, apart from their theoretical flaws, have other shortcomings as well. Since their introduction in the 1940s TLVs have been lowered over the years. For example, from 1945 to 1988 the benzene TLV dropped from 100 ppm to 10 ppm, while the vinyl chloride TLV fell from 500 ppm to only 5 ppm. [24] Such drastic reductions in TLVs raise concerns about their validity for other chemicals.

In a 1986 study by Roach and Rappaport TLVs were shown to be problematic. The study concluded 425 of 3077 (13.8%) workers suffered impairment to their health following exposure at or below the TLV. [25] Likewise, Roach and Rappaport discovered 38 of 161 (23.6%) workers suffered some irritation following exposure at or below the TLV. [25] As a result they concluded TLVs do not represent a "threshold" at all but a compromised level of "safety" that is misleading. Roach and Rappaport recommended average worker exposure be kept to a fraction (1/4 to 1/10) of the suggested TLV.

In another study by Castleman and Ziem TLVs came under scrutiny for another reason. Their study examined how TLVs are set and concluded the process is highly favourable toward industry rather than labour. Castleman and Ziem found TLV committee representatives are often industry-employed health professionals who often set standards with industry's best interests in mind. Again, this study concluded TLVs are not reliable.

TLVs are not the most accurate measure of carcinogens in the workplace. They generate a false sense of security by creating the impression that a substance is safe at a certain level. A worker may in fact be at risk of developing cancer if he/she relies on TLVs.

3: STATISTICALLY SPEAKING

3.1 THE STATS ON THE MATTER

The following tables and graphs provide a statistical overview of cancer in Canada and throughout the world. The aim of this section is to illustrate how cancer is a serious health issue in general and among certain occupations in particular. For the purposes of this report, and to avoid being swamped by numbers, the statistics reported typically represent selected findings rather than complete presentations of studies. As well, the statistics are presented in a simple, direct way to enable quick interpretation and discussion.

3A CAUSES OF DEATH IN CANADA (1992)

The statistics represented by the following graphs [1] indicate cancer was the second leading cause of death among Canadians in 1992. Only cumulative heart diseases claimed more lives than cancer. Also, as the percentages indicate, more than one in four deaths in Canada were attributed to cancer in 1992. This ratio is now estimated to have climbed closer to one in three deaths or more than 30% of all deaths are now likely due to cancer. In raw numbers there were 152.7 female deaths per 100,000 and 244 male deaths per 100,000 caused by cancer in 1992. [1] Despite the fact that cancer claimed almost an equal percentage of deaths for men and women in 1992, there were considerably more men who died from the disease.

CAUSES OF DEATH IN CANADA (MEN, 1992)

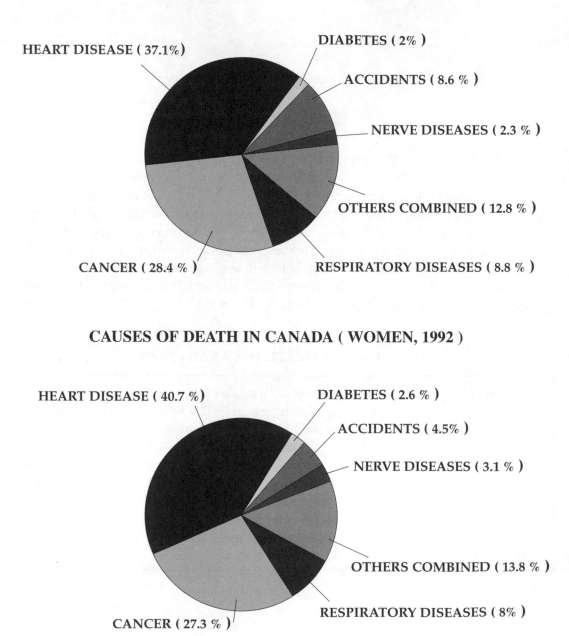

HEART DISEASE (37.1%)

DIABETES (2%)

ACCIDENTS (8.6 %)

NERVE DISEASES (2.3 %)

OTHERS COMBINED (12.8 %)

CANCER (28.4 %)

RESPIRATORY DISEASES (8.8 %)

CAUSES OF DEATH IN CANADA (WOMEN, 1992)

HEART DISEASE (40.7 %)

DIABETES (2.6 %)

ACCIDENTS (4.5%)

NERVE DISEASES (3.1 %)

OTHERS COMBINED (13.8 %)

RESPIRATORY DISEASES (8%)

CANCER (27.3 %)

32

3B LEADING TYPES OF CANCER DEATHS

Both of the following graphs [1] break down the various leading types of cancer causing deaths among men and women in Canada in 1992. Breast and lung cancer each caused almost 20% of all cancer deaths among women. With men, lung cancer was the leading cause of cancer death by a wide margin, followed by prostate cancer. Also, comparing 1992 cancer statistics to 1988, there were 7,500 more deaths and 21,700 more new cases of cancer in 1992 compared to 1988.

LEADING CANCER DEATHS (MALES 1992)

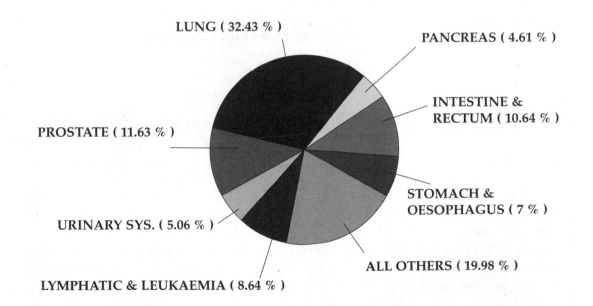

LUNG (32.43 %)

PANCREAS (4.61 %)

INTESTINE & RECTUM (10.64 %)

PROSTATE (11.63 %)

STOMACH & OESOPHAGUS (7 %)

URINARY SYS. (5.06 %)

ALL OTHERS (19.98 %)

LYMPHATIC & LEUKAEMIA (8.64 %)

LEADING CANCER DEATHS (FEMALES 1992)

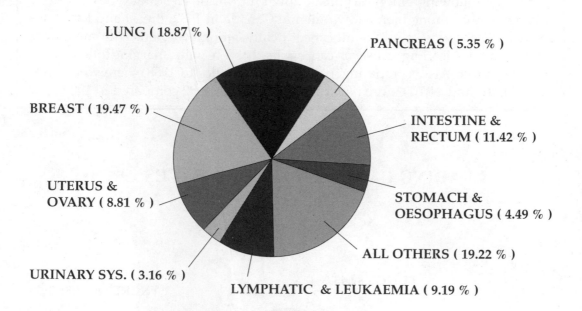

LUNG (18.87 %)

PANCREAS (5.35 %)

BREAST (19.47 %)

INTESTINE &
RECTUM (11.42 %)

UTERUS &
OVARY (8.81 %)

STOMACH &
OESOPHAGUS (4.49 %)

ALL OTHERS (19.22 %)

URINARY SYS. (3.16 %)

LYMPHATIC & LEUKAEMIA (9.19 %)

3C PERCENTAGE OF DEATHS CAUSED BY CANCER IN CANADA

The two following graphs depict various aspects of the percentages of deaths caused by cancer. The first graph illustrates how the percentage of deaths caused by cancer for both men and women in Canada has risen constantly over the past sixty years from the 10-12% range in the early 1930s to present rates which hover around 30%. [26, 27, 2] The second graph indicates how common cancer deaths were among various age groups. Cancer caused in excess of 35% of all deaths and was the leading cause of death for women aged 35-69. For women aged 50-54, cancer caused 56.9% of all deaths. Cancer was also the leading cause of death among males aged 45-64 and was responsible for 25-40% of all deaths among males aged 45-84. [1]

% OF DEATHS CAUSED BY CANCER
1931- 1992

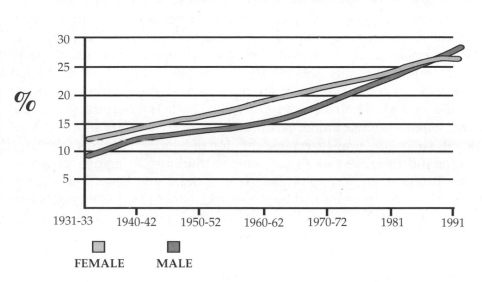

FEMALE   MALE

% OF DEATHS CAUSED BY CANCER
BY AGE AND SEX (1992)

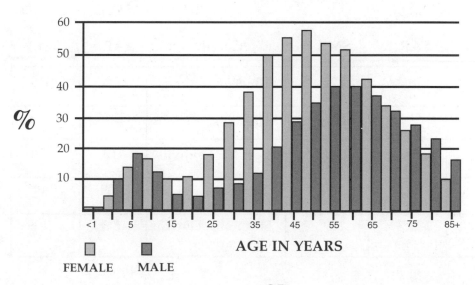

AGE IN YEARS

FEMALE   MALE

35

3D CANCER RATES IN CANADA

The following table [28] shows many Ontario regions/counties had higher than expected cancer mortality rates from 1975-86, based on Average of Age Specific Rates (AAR) a measure used to minimize differences in age when comparing populations and Standard Mortality Rate (SMR) where any rate above 100 is a higher than expected rate. As well, there was a large difference between the highest and lowest rates (i.e. males Cochrane: AAR 196.8, SMR 121 vs Haliburton: AAR 131.1, SMR 76, and females Timiskaming: AAR 127.4, SMR 115 vs Manitoulin: AAR 101.5, SMR 85). There is also an over representation of regions/counties with large mining and/or industrial sectors (e.g. Cochrane, Sudbury, Algoma, Nipissing, Thunder Bay, Timiskaming, Hamilton-Wentworth, Brant and Essex). Related to this matter is a 1995 report published by the Essex District Health Council which found a 30% higher death rate for Essex County males caused by lung cancer, despite smoking habits similar to the provincial average. [29]

HIGHEST CANCER MORTALITY RATES PER 100,000 PEOPLE AMONG ONTARIO COUNTIES & REGIONAL MUNICIPALITIES
ALL CANCER SITES (1975-1986)

MALE			FEMALE		
Reg/Count	AAR	SMR	Reg/Count	AAR	SMR
Cochrane	196.8	121	Timiskaming	127.4	115
Sudbury	179.4	112	Dufferin	122.3	112
Algoma	181.0	112	Leeds & Grenville	120.3	109
Rainy River	176.3	110	Nipissing	115.9	108
Hastings	177.7	109	Stormont/Dundas Glengarry	118.3	105

Nipissing	176.8	109	Muskoka	118.2	105
Brant	173.7	107	Brant	116.5	105
Ham./Went.	173.1	107	Thunder Bay	112.9	104
Essex	170.9	105	Frontenac	111.4	103
Kent	171.2	105	Cochrane	112.1	103

* The AAR & SMR levels may vary from the ranking order as rankings are determined by statistical confidence levels.

3E CANCER RATES IN SELECTED COUNTRIES

The statistics represented by the following graph [30] indicate Canada is not alone with respect to increasing rates of death due to cancer. All of the countries sampled experienced elevated percentages of deaths caused by cancer from 1955 to 1986. The levels of cancer deaths in Japan were particularly high, as both female and male rates more than doubled in just thirty-one years. It is clear that cancer is becoming a world wide health concern of epidemic proportions as it claims a greater and greater percentage of deaths. Moreover, all of the countries sampled below are industrialized nations with significant industrial sectors, huge blue collar workforces and widespread environmental pollution problems. The cancer situation among developing countries which have been industrializing rapidly in the post World War II era (e.g. India, China, Indonesia) is much worse than the countries sampled in Graph 3E. Statistics for these countries are not available at this time, however. One of the issues for developing countries is that industrial development is not being accompanied by adequate health and safety and environmental programmes. In countries stricken with large debts and deteriorating structural adjustment programmes this issue is critical. All of this evidence suggests cancer has become a health issue that spans the globe.

MALE CANCER RATES, SELECTED COUNTRIES

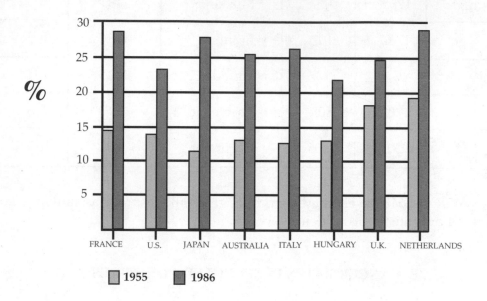

%

1955   1986

3.2 A LOOK AT CANCER IN THE AUTO INDUSTRY

Cancer in the auto industry is a critical issue. High rates of cancer among auto workers demonstrate how the disease is linked to industrial processes. Recent studies discovered excessive levels of respiratory and digestive cancers among auto workers exposed to cutting fluids (also known as machining fluids). Cutting fluids pose a problem because high speed machining and grinding creates oil mists that are inhaled by workers. Cutting fluids are also hazardous because their composition is often a complex combination of substances, many of which may be carcinogenic.

Evidence of lung and laryngeal cancer caused by inhaling oil mist was first documented by A. Southam in 1928. In a more recent study the Hydra-Matic plant in Ypsilanti, Michigan was one of the operations assessed by a group of Harvard University researchers led by E. Eisen. Their research found white male auto workers suffered an 85% higher incidence of laryngeal (voice-box) cancer. [33] Among workers at the same plant exposed for 20 and 30 years, the rates of laryngeal cancer increased to 114% and 210% higher than the national average. [33] The same study also revealed pancreatic cancer levels among black male auto workers in the Gear and Axle plant in Hamtramck, Michigan to be 70% higher than expected levels. [33] In an updated study, Dr. Eisen's research team detected a 123% higher incidence of laryngeal cancer among auto workers in three Michigan plants combined. [34] This rate increased to a 151% higher incidence of laryngeal cancer among workers with 10-20 years of exposure. [34] Similar rates of excessive cancer among auto workers exposed to cutting fluids have been detected in Sweden. The Harvard study, meanwhile, also found higher than expected rates of leukaemia, as well as brain, liver and lung cancer among auto workers.

Cutting Fluids: Excess Cancer

The Harvard study of 46,000 Michigan GM workers is the most extensive investigation into the cancer risks of cutting fluids exposed workers. This study found statistically significant excesses of laryngeal, rectal, oesophagus and pancreas cancer among cutting fluids exposed populations. United Auto Workers (UAW) union members have participated in nine mortality studies where cutting fluids were in use. In seven out of nine studies excess stomach cancer was found. (31) In Ontario the Occupational Disease Panel (ODP) has issued a report on cutting fluids and laryngeal cancer. The ODP believes the scientific evidence is strong enough to recommend that the disease be placed in Schedule 3 of the Workers' Compensation Act. The ODP noted that "not only were there increases, but the majority of the studies show levels of excess *double* the expected, particularly when the time since first exposure is greater than 20 years." The Panel is preparing further reports on the relationship between cutting fluids and cancer.

Cutting fluids are the principal causal agent in all of these findings. The link between occupational practices and high incidence of cancer is clearly demonstrated among auto workers.

3.3 CANCER AND BLUE COLLAR WORKERS

Many studies and statistics indicate that occupational cancer is particularly common among blue collar workers. Dr. Peter Infante of the Occupational Safety and Health Administration of the U.S. Department of Labour maintains blue collar workers are suffering the most and being treated like test subjects for the effects of industrial chemicals. Dr. Infante summarized his position while testifying before the U.S. President's Cancer Panel in 1994 when he stated:

Much as canaries were once taken into mines to warn of imminent danger from falling oxygen levels or rising levels of toxic fumes, blue-collar workers in this society are now being used to identify chemical carcinogens in the general environment. [16]

This point is supported by IARC which compiles lists of carcinogens. With respect to lung cancer, of the 22 substances or human processes that have been identified by IARC as lung carcinogens, 21 (95%) have been identified as a result of case reports or epidemiologic studies of workers. [16] As well, of all carcinogens (apart from carcinogenic medicinal drugs) 34 of 44 (77%) have been identified by IARC as a consequence of studies on workers. [16] This indicates that most of the knowledge regarding which substances and processes cause cancer has been

40

obtained from studies involving workers.

Dr. Infante suggests occupational cancer is being largely ignored because blue collar workers rather than white collar professionals are at the greatest risk. As such, he argues occupational cancer is a health issue and a socio-political issue. Dr. Infante maintains that the high incidence of cancer deaths among blue collar workers is also an indication of more widespread cancer to come in the future. He recommends, among other strategies, that detailed occupational histories be collected by cancer registries to help recognize the relationship between occupational exposures and cancer. It is imperative, according to Dr. Infante, to react to the obvious signals among blue-collar workers and take stronger measures to prevent occupational cancer.

Cancer Among Firefighters

A report published by the Occupational Disease Panel in September 1994 examined the evidence associated with firefighting and cancer and cardiovascular disease. The report concluded probable connections exist between firefighting and brain, lymphatic and haematopoietic, colon, bladder and kidney cancer and firefighting. The evidence for the elevated rates of brain cancer among firefighters were particularly high due to vinyl chloride, formaldehyde and acrylonitrile exposures at fire sites. Some studies reported brain cancer rates 2-5 times higher than expected among firefighters. Elevated rates of lymphatic and haematopoietic cancer were associated with benzene inhalation at fire sites. (35)

3.4 NON-INDUSTRIAL OCCUPATIONAL CANCER

Occupational cancer is not reserved to workers in heavy industry. Carcinogenic substances are present in a wide variety of workplaces. For example, low level exposure to antineoplastic drugs used to treat cancer patients has been linked to chromosomal abnormalities which may be linked to cancer. A study conducted by Dr. S. Milkovic-Kraus and Dr. D. Horvat of nurses working in oncology units with daily exposure to antineoplastic drugs discovered significant differences in sister chromated exchanges, a type of genetic injury which is linked to environmental cancer. [36] The nurses studied by Dr. Milkovic-Kraus and Dr. Horvat were exposed to cyclophosphamide (a Group 1 IARC carcinogen), adriamycin (a Group 2A IARC carcinogen) and cisplatinum (a Group 2A IARC carcinogen).

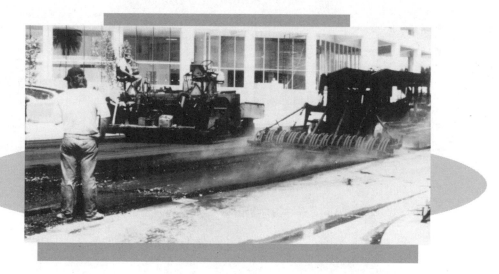

Other non-industrial occupations are also at risk of carcinogen exposure. Formaldehyde, which is used in a number of medically related occupations (e.g. pathologists, medical laboratory technicians, chemists and morticians), is a Group 2A IARC carcinogen and has been linked to lung, bladder and prostate cancer.

Significant excesses of lung and stomach cancer and leukaemia have been detected among roofers exposed to asphalt, bitumen fumes and hot pitch containing PAHs. [37] As well, studies involving laundry and garment cleaning workers have found significant associations with non-Hodgkins lymphoma and exposure to benzene and other solvents. [38] Another possible source of non-industrial occupational carcinogen exposure is radiation from video display terminals and other electrical sources.

Many of these cancer risks have yet to be fully explored. The point here, however, is that non-industrial workers are certainly not excluded from occupational cancer risks.

3.5 MAKING SENSE OF THE NUMBERS

It is possible to fill many pages with statistics from studies conducted around the world that all point to a strong relationship between occupation and a high incidence of cancer. Likewise, there are many studies that argue a one-hundred percent proof positive causal connection between cancer and occupation cannot be illustrated. So which statistics and which studies are correct? The answer is simple. If we are concerned with reducing cancer risks, we cannot wait until every scientist, every employer and every researcher agrees that occupationally caused cancer is a reality. Instead, it must be acknowledged now that too many studies indicate a strong association between occupation and cancer and we must move on to eliminating risks and saving workers' lives. The standard for action should be the same as that used in other fields of medicine. We should not wait until the legal test of "beyond a reasonable doubt" has been met.

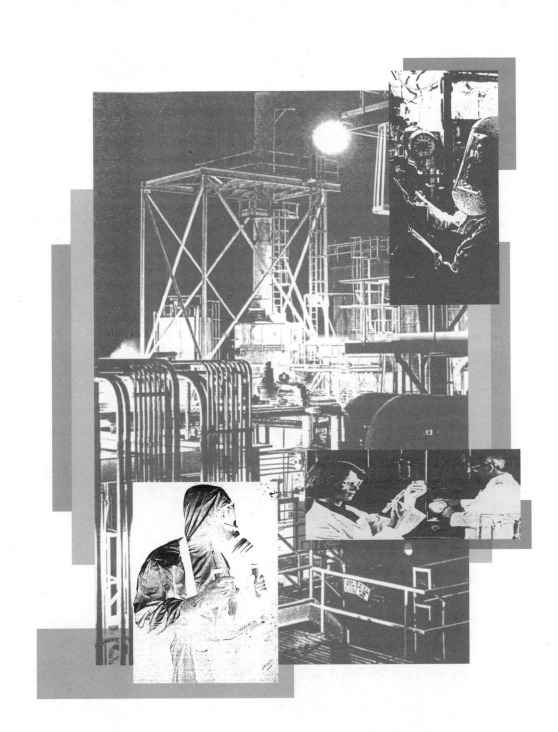

4: REDUCING CANCER RISKS

The next step is to move on to solutions for preventing cancer in the workplace. The following is a list of some of the basic measures to reduce the risk of occupational cancer.

4.1 WHAT YOU CAN DO

1) Risk Assessment. Workers can assess their workplace risks by reading product labels and Material Safety Data Sheets, researching the product and asking Health and Safety representatives, union stewards, supervisors, hygienists and/or doctors about a substance or industrial process.

2) Set standards. Once a substance is identified as carcinogenic, determine acceptable levels of exposure to the carcinogen, depending on whether it is a highly carcinogenic substance, or less carcinogenic.

3) Contact your Health and Safety Committee or local union steward. Contact these workplace representatives to determine if they are aware of carcinogens on the job and discuss strategies to reduce or eliminate carcinogen exposure risks, such as enclosure, exhaust ventilation and process re-design.

4) Reduce exposure and substitute with a non-carcinogen. This is the easiest and most direct way to eliminate the risk of cancer on the job. If a substance is a known carcinogen and you work with it, then eliminate your exposure by removing the carcinogen and using a non-carcinogenic substitute product. Or, and this option is less favourable, use personal protective equipment (this includes every-

47

thing from safety gloves to ventilators) to safe-guard workers from exposure to the substance. Protective equipment should be checked periodically to ensure it is functioning properly.

5) Workplace monitoring. Inspections should be conducted to ensure safety. This includes ensuring air quality and general safety practices are being enforced.

6) Medical consultation. Older workers and retirees should have their health assessed regularly due to the latency period often associated with cancer. Early detection of certain types of cancer may result in increased survival rates. Consulting doctors who consider occupation and work history as crucial components of an individual's health history is essential as well. If your doctor does not ask about your work history, offer this information to her/him or switch to another physician.

Cancer Watch Groups

Epidemiology does not have to be left to the medical and scientific professionals. Groups of auto workers in Ohio and Michigan decided to conduct their own investigation after they noticed a pattern of cancer among their co-workers. Workers Against Toxic Chemical Hazards (WATCH), a rank and file auto workers group in Lordstown, Ohio, compiled a revealing list of cancer deaths among auto workers using only the obituaries from local newspapers.

Another cancer WATCH group in Ypsilanti carried out an investigation after a cluster of brain cancer cases emerged in a small section of the plant. Their activities forced General Motors to expand a study of cutting fluid mortality by Harvard University to include examinations of brain cancer.

Excess cancer risk was confirmed in both cases proving once again that the workers' instincts and experience concerning occupational health hazards are often confirmed.

7) Promote good health. In addition to reducing risks on the job, workers should also try to reduce other environmental risks linked to cancer (e.g. tobacco, diet, exposure to environmental pollutants). It is important for workers to promote a healthy lifestyle on the job and away from the job. Employers should be active in promoting good health as well by implementing measures such as a smoke-free work environment and providing nutritious food in the cafeteria, if one exists in the workplace.

8) Educate yourself. This is a very broad preventative measure and also the cornerstone of all other preventative measures. Workers must take the initiative to educate themselves about risks on the job. Education includes knowing your rights under the Occupational Health and Safety Act. Education includes informing other workers and your employers about potential risks. It also means reporting risks and taking action to help promote a safe and healthy workplace.

9) Take action. This is, again, a broad term which may repeat some points already made. It cannot be emphasized enough, however, that a healthy worker is one who learns about the substances she/he works with and takes steps to reduce risks. Workers can form cancer action groups, they can contact occupational health agencies to learn about cancer (and programmes to eliminate cancer risks) and spread the word no worker should put themselves at risk of developing cancer on the job, the costs are just too great.

4.2 WINDSOR REGIONAL CANCER CENTRE PROGRAMME

As a means to strengthen the relationship between cancer and occupation, a unique programme has been initiated in Windsor through the collaborative efforts of the Windsor Regional Cancer Centre, the Ontario Occupational Disease Panel and the Occupational Health Clinics for Ontario Workers (Windsor). The programme is the first of its kind in Canada as it will employ a computer touch screen programme to compile cancer patients' work histories. Patients at the Centre will enter their work histories with the help of a user-friendly computer programme where they will be guided through a series of questions related to their employment history.

One of the main reasons a causal relationship between cancer and occupation has not been widely accepted is due to the lack of documentation of employment exposure histories among cancer patients. This new programme will address this information shortage.

During the pilot stage of the project each patient will complete a questionnaire to help assess the accuracy of the programme. OHCOW staff will also conduct interviews with groups of patients to test the effectiveness of the programme. For the undertaking to be successful it is crucial that other cancer centres in Ontario and across Canada launch similar programmes. Prior to this project, occupational histories have been largely neglected as a factor in diagnosing disease and treating patients. Through this endeavour more will be learned about cancer, particularly its relationship to a person's occupation.

5: RELATED ISSUES

5.1 THE ENVIRONMENTAL CONTEXT

The purpose of this book is to raise awareness of occupational cancer among workers, employers and the public. To fully understand cancer it is also necessary to consider the wider environmental context.

While cancer is an ancient disease that can be traced back to human tissue in Egyptian mummies and even, some believe, to dinosaurs, never has it been a more common cause of death than in the twentieth century. [13] This has lead some medical researchers to conclude that the prevalence of cancer today is a result of an increasingly industrialized global society. This theory is known as the environmental position for explaining high rates of cancer.

The accumulation of toxic materials in the air, water, soil and food supply is often acknowledged as a risk to human health. The main trouble with toxic materials is their persistence in the natural environment. Toxic materials remain in the natural environment for long periods of time, often because they cannot be metabolized and detoxified (broken down). Instead, toxins tend to accumulate in plants, animals and humans; a process known as bioconcentration. Humans, occupying the top spot on the food chain, are at particular risk of bioconcentration. When these toxins accumulate in the natural environment and become more widespread they may cause cancer rates to increase as well.

A number of studies have identified high rates of cancer caused by environmental pollution. For example: excessive lung cancer rates have been identified in communities in close proximity to petrochemical plants, ecological studies have indicated high rates of breast cancer among residents living close to hazardous waste sites, a study by R. D. Morris in the U.S. pointed to water disinfectant by-products as a source of bladder and rectal cancer and a 1993 study by L. M. Keiding acknowledged emissions from cars and other combustion engines contain a number of suspected carcinogenic agents (e.g. benzene, polycyclic aromatic hydrocarbons) that contribute to high rates of lung cancer. [39]

Studies of wildlife populations also reveal the dangers of toxic materials in the natural environment. Fish and birds exposed to industrial chemicals and pollutants, in particular, have shown high rates of birth defects and reproductive disorders which are considered an early warning of potential increases in cancer rates. [39] As well, fish caught in the Great Lakes are often laden with tumours. These signals reveal the poor health of the natural environment and the prevalence of toxic contamination.

There is some uncertainty regarding exactly how much of today's high cancer rates may be caused by environmental factors. Estimates of environmental causation of cancer vary from 20% to close to 90%. These factors include: pollution, sunlight, occupation, pesticides and other elements. One problem with the environmental position is that from a purely scientific perspective, a number of obstacles (e.g. the accuracy of exposure assessments, the lack of control over study populations and the long time required for study results) inhibit determining the certainty of environmental toxins causing cancer. Most researchers assert,

Pesticide Hazards

Pesticides have been linked to adverse human health effects from both occupational exposure during spraying and harvesting and from ingestion. A number of pesticides have been used without full knowledge of their health/environmental effects. Many have subsequently been banned from use (e.g. DDT). In some developing regions of the world, restrictions on hazardous pesticides are not as strict as they are in developed countries such as Canada. In nations hampered with chronic food shortages, banning substances that (on the surface) seem to assist agricultural development is not a simple matter. As a result, hazardous pesticide use in the developing world has become a serious concern. A recent World Health Organization study estimates there were 3 million cases of severe pesticide poisoning causing 220,000 deaths in 1990. The WHO stated 99% of the deaths occurred in developing countries. (13) The pesticide issue indicates occupational and environmental cancer risks are becoming a problem of epidemic proportion in the developing world.

tainty of environmental toxins causing cancer. Most researchers assert, however, that in order to exercise caution, a "weight of evidence" approach should be adopted, whereby the results from different types of studies (e.g. wildlife studies, laboratory research, epidemiological studies) are each given weight in assessing the potential for cancer caused by environmental factors.

The key to reducing the risk of environmentally induced cancer is to prevent the use and generation of toxic substances. Since it is not possible to retrieve many toxins from the natural environment, attention must be directed toward eliminating the use of toxins and thereby preventing their introduction into the natural environment. This means targeting the sources of toxins. Some ways of achieving this include:

Breast Cancer & the Environment

Increased rates of breast cancer are one example of how cancer and environmental pollution go hand in hand. In North America a woman's likelihood of contracting breast cancer has doubled over one generation to the point where breast cancer is now the leading cause of cancer death among Canadian women. The abundance of organochlorines in the environment is closely linked to high rates of breast cancer. Organochlorines are found in plastics, pesticides, herbicides, paper products, preservation agents and tampons. Organochlorines pose a threat to humans because they accumulate in living tissue. Since humans are at the top of the food chain, concentrations of organochlorines tend to be particularly high in humans. The link between organochlorines and breast cancer occurs because organochlorines are capable of imitating oestrogen. The danger here is that high oestrogen levels are associated with breast cancer. Because organochlorines trigger similar biological responses in breast tissue as oestrogen they may be a contributing factor to increased rates of breast cancer this century. (40)

Δ   Integrate pollution prevention with industrial policy to ensure that industrial developmentprogresses toward the objective of eliminating bio concentrating toxic substances.

Δ   Stricter standards for controlling environmental carcinogens should be developed and implemented in Canada and other industrialized (izing) nations.

Δ   Support the development and application of alternative, non-chemical pest control measures as a means to phase out toxic pesticide use.

Δ   Impose regulatory limits on radioactive toxins using the same methodology and standards applied to chemical contaminants.

Δ   Vehicular emissions (i.e. from cars, trucks, motorcycles, lawnmowers, chainsaws, motorboats and minibikes) must be reduced to cut down on toxic air contamination from benzene and polycyclic aromatic hydrocarbons.

Δ   Industrialized nations, such as Canada, should stop exporting hazardous technologies and products to developing countries.

Δ   Multinational corporations should apply health and safety and environmental standards in developing countries that are not lower than those they use in developed countries, such as Canada.

Δ   Encourage alternative, efficient, non-polluting modes of transportation (e.g. walking, bicycles and public transit). [39]

To fully combat cancer, carcinogens must be reduced in both the workplace and the natural environment. There is no point in separating the many sources of environmental cancer into smaller categories. Environmental pollution must be regarded as a whole. A healthy workplace is only beneficial within a healthy natural environment.

6: CONCLUSION

6.1 ACT NOW

Cancer, because it is largely environmentally caused, can strike anyone. Any person who is exposed to carcinogenic substances over an extended period of time is at risk of developing cancer. It is really this simple.

Occupational hazards are a significant contributing factor to increased levels of environmentally caused cancer this century. There can be little doubt that continuous exposure to carcinogens on the job may lead to increased rates of cancer.

The solution to reducing high levels of cancer is to clean up the environment by eliminating carcinogens. Likewise, the solution on the job is to reduce exposure, or better yet, substitute non-carcinogenic materials for carcinogenic materials.

Knowing about the hazards posed by carcinogenic substances used on the job is not enough. This knowledge must be acted upon. Workers who identify carcinogenic hazards on their job must take the next step and eliminate cancer risks. In the same way that neighbourhoods and communities object to toxic dumps and foul industrial emissions, workers must not tolerate occupational carcinogens. The risks are simply too great. Act now and eliminate the risks.

CONTACTS & RESOURCES

The following organizations and publications may be able to provide additional information concerning occupational cancer, other occupational health and safety and environmental issues and your rights in the workplace.

ORGANIZATIONS:

Windsor Occupational Health Information Service (WOHIS)
547 Victoria Avenue, Windsor, Ontario, N9A 4N1, Tel. (519) 254-5157, Fax (519) 254-4192

Occupational Health Clinics for Ontario Workers (OHCOW) (four clinics):
547 Victoria Avenue, Windsor, Ontario, N9A 4N1, Tel. (519) 973-4800, Toll Free: 1-800-565-3185, Fax (519) 973-1906

848 Main Street East, Hamilton, Ontario, L8M 1L9, Tel. (905) 549-2552, Toll Free: 1-800-263-2129, Fax (905) 549-7993

1478 Danforth Avenue, Toronto, Ontario, M4J 1N4, Tel. (416) 778-4394, Fax (416) 778-6557

1780 Regent Street South, Sudbury, Ontario, P3E 3Z8, Tel. (705) 523-2330, Fax (705) 522-8957

Canadian Auto Workers
205 Placer Court, Willowdale, Ontario, M2H 3H9, Tel. 1-800-268-5763, Fax (416) 495-6554

Canadian Centre for Occupational Health and Safety
250 Main Street East, Hamilton, Ontario, L8N 1H6, Tel. (905) 570-8094, Toll Free 1-800-668-4284, Fax (905) 572-2206, E-mail: custserv@ccohs.ca

Canadian Labour Congress

2841 Riverside Drive, Ottawa, Ontario, K1V 8X7, Tel. (613) 521-3400, Fax (613) 521-4655

Canadian Union of Public Employees
21 Florence Street, Ottawa, Ontario, K2P 0W6, Tel. (613) 237-1590, Fax (613) 237-5508

Citizens Environmental Alliance
P.O. Box 548, Station A, Windsor, Ontario, N9A 6M6, Tel. (519) 973-1116

London Hazards Centre
Interchange Studios, Dalby Street, London, U.K., NW5 3NQ, Tel. 0171 267 3387, E-mail: LONHAZ@MCR1.geomail.or/@gn:apc.org.

London Occupational Safety & Health Information Service
222 - 424 Wellington Street, London, Ontario, N6A 3P3, Tel. (519) 433-4156, Fax (519) 433-2887

Manitoba Federation of Labour
Occupational Health Centre Inc., 102-275 Broadway, Winnipeg, Manitoba, R3C 4M6, Tel. (204) 949-0811, Fax (204) 956-0848

Occupational Disease Panel
69 Yonge Street, Suite 1004, Toronto, Ontario, M5E 1K3, Tel. (416) 327-4156

Ontario Public Service Employees Union
100 Lesmill Road, North York, Ontario, M3B 3P8, Tel. (416) 443-8888, Fax (416) 443-0553

Toronto Workers Health and Safety Centre
15 Gervais Drive, Suite 102, Don Mills, Ontario, M3C 1Y8, Tel. (416) 441-1939, Fax (416) 441-1043

There are also workers health and safety centres in Cambridge, Hamilton, Kingston, Ottawa, Sarnia, Sudbury, Oshawa and Thunder Bay.

Toronto Workers' Health & Safety Legal Clinic

180 Dundas Street West, Suite 201, Toronto, Ontario, M5G 1Z8, Tel. (416) 971-8832, Fax (416) 971-8834

United Steelworkers of America
200 Ronson Drive, Etobicoke, Ontario, M9W 5Z9, Tel. (416) 243-8792, Fax (416) 243-9573

PUBLICATIONS

The following publications provide additional information on occupational cancer and other occupational health and safety concerns.

Cancer Wars
Robert N. Proctor (Author), Basic Books: 1995.

Hunter's Diseases of Occupations
P.A.B. Raffle, W.R. Lee, R.I. McCallum, R. Murray (Editors), Edward Arnold Publishing: 1991.

IARC Monographs on the Evaluation of Carcinogenic Risks to Humans (List of IARC Evaluations)
World Health Organisation, International Agency for Research on Cancer: June 1995.

New Solutions
A Journal of Environmental and Occupational Health Policy, Work Environment Programme, University of Massachusetts Lowell, Lowell, MA, 01863, Tel. (508) 934-3263.

Occupational Health and Safety Act (and other related Government Publications)
Government of Ontario: November 1992, (Available at WOHIS).

Occupational Health & Safety Canada
A bi-monthly periodical published by Southam Incorporated.

Occupational Medicine
Carl Zenz (Editor), Mosby Year Book: 1988.

Prevention of Occupational Cancer
CRC Press Incorporated: 1981.

Report to the Workers' Compensation Board on Cardiovascular Disease and Cancer Among Firefighters
Industrial Disease Standards Panel: September 1994.

Report to the Workers' Compensation Board on Lung Cancer in the Hardrock Mining Industry
Industrial Disease Standards Panel: March 1994.

Report to the Workers' Compensation Board on the Health Effects of Occupational Exposure to Petroleum-based fluids used for Machining and Lubricating Metal in Manufacturing: Cancer of the Larynx
Occupational Disease Panel: June 1995.

Risk Factors for Cancer in the Workplace
CRC Press Incorporated: 1991.

Seventh Annual Report on Carcinogens (Summary 1994)
U.S. Department of Health and Human Services: 1994.

The Global Guardian
(CAW Windsor Regional Environment Council Publication)
581 St. Pierre Street, Tecumseh, Ontario, N8N 1Z2, Tel. (519) 735-6684, Fax (519) 251-1388.

The Politics of Cancer
Samuel Epstein (Author), Anchor Press: 1979.

Work and Health: The Inside Story
c/o WOHIS, 547 Victoria Avenue, Windsor, Ontario, N9A 4N1, Tel. (519) 254-5157, Fax (519) 254-4192.

An occupational health and safety and environmental newsletter published three times a year by the Windsor Occupational Health Information Service.

Workers' Health International Newsletter (WHIN)
P.O. Box 199, Sheffield, S1 1FQ, England, Tel. +44 114 276 5695, Fax +44 114 276 7257. Spanish language edition of WHIN is available from WHIN en Espanol, Gabinete de Salud Laboral de CC.OO.P.V., Plaza Napoles y Sicilia 5, 46003 Valencia, Spain.

REFERENCES

1) *Mortality - Summary List of Causes* (1992) Ottawa: Statistics Canada, Catalogue 84-209.

2) Epstein, Samuel (1979) *The Politics of Cancer*, Garden City, NY: Anchor Press.

3) *Cancer Facts And Figures 1994,* American Cancer Society.

4) *Canadian Cancer Statistics 1992* (1992) Toronto: National Institute of Cancer.

5) Shaw, Charles A. (1981) "What is Cancer and How Much is Caused by Occupational Exposure?" in *Prevention of Occupational Cancer*, Boca Raton: CRC Press.

6) Siemiatycki, Jack (1991) "Introduction to Occupational Cancer" in *Risk Factors for Cancer in the Workplace*, Boca Raton: CRC Press.

7) Selikoff, I. J. (1977) "Cancer Risks of Asbestos Exposure" in *Origins of Human Cancer*, Vol. 4, H. H. Hiatt, J. D. Watson & J. A. Winsten editors: Cold Spring Harbour Laboratory.

8) *The Asbestos Hazards Handbook* (1995) London: London Hazards Centre.

9) "Subcommittee on Crime of the Committee on the Judiciary" House of Representatives, Ninety-Sixth Congress, Second Session, Corporate Crime, Washington: United States Government Printing Office, May, 1980.

10) Ozonoff, David (1988) "Failed Warnings: Asbestos Related Disease and Industrial Medicine" in *The Health and Safety of Workers,* London: Oxford University Press.

11) "Breath Taken" in *Health/PAY Bulletin*, Winter, 1990.

12) "Preventing Breast Cancer", in *Rachel's Environment and Health Weekly* # 418, Annapolis MD: Environmental Research Foundation.

13) Proctor, Robert N. (1995) *Cancer Wars*, New York: Basic Books.

14) *Report to the Workers' Compensation Board on Cardiovascular Disease and*

Cancer Among Firefighters, Industrial Disease Standards Panel, Toronto.

15) Siemiatycki, Jack, Warholder, Sholom, De War, Ronald, Cardis, Elizabeth, Greenwood, Celia & Richardson, Lesley (1988) "Degree of Confounding Bias Related to Smoking, Ethnic Group and Socio-Economic Status in Estimates of the Assumption Between Occupation and Cancer" *Journal of Occupational Medicine*, 30: 617-625.

16) Infante, Peter F. (1995) "Cancer and Blue-Collar Workers: Who Cares?" in *New Solutions*, Vol. 5, No. 2, Winter 1995.

17) Swartz, Joel B. & Epstein, Samuel (1995) "What is Responsible for the Rise in Lung Cancer Mortality?" in *New Solutions*, Vol. 5, No. 3: 62-70.

18) *IARC Monographs on the Evaluation of Carcinogenic Risks to Humans (Volume 60: Some Industrial Chemicals)* (1994): World Health Organization, International Agency for Research on Cancer.

19) Paci, Eugenio (1995) "Have We Lost the Meaning? Questions Around Epidemiologic Practice" in *New Solutions*, Vol. 6, No. 1: 35-40.

20) Olsen, Jorn, Merletti, Franco, Snashall, David & Vuylsteek, Karel (1991) *Searching for Causes of Work-Related Disease: An Introduction to Epidemiology at the Work Site*, Oxford: Oxford University Press.

21) Zahm, Sheila H., Pottern, Linda M., Lewis, Denise R., Ward, Mary, H., White, Deborah, W., "Inclusion of Women and Minorities in Occupational Cancer Epidemiologic Research" in *Journal of Occupational Medicine*, Vol. 36, No. 8, August 1994: 842-847.

22) *U.I.C.C. XVI International Cancer Conference*; October 30 - November 5 1994: New Delhi.

23) *IARC Monographs on the Evaluation of Carcinogenic Risks to Humans* (1995) Lyon: World Health Organization, International Agency for Research on Cancer.

24) Castleman, Barry I. & Ziem, Grace E. (1988) "Corporate Influence on Threshold Limit Values" *American Journal of Industrial Medicine*, 13: 531-559.

25) Roach, S.A. & Rappaport, S.M. (1990) "But They Are Not Thresholds: A Critical Analysis of the Documentation of Threshold Limit Values" *American*

Journal of Industrial Medicine, 17: 727-753.

26) *Cancer Patterns in Canada 1931-1974* (1975) Ottawa: Ministry of National Health and Welfare.

27) *Women in Canada - Third Edition* (1995) Ottawa: Statistics Canada, Catalogue 89-503E.

28) *Geographic Distribution of Cancer in Ontario, Volume 1: Atlas of Cancer Mortality 1976-1985* (1991) Toronto: The Ontario Cancer Treatment and Research Foundation.

29) *A Picture of Health: The 1995 Health Profile of Windsor-Essex County Residents* (1995) Windsor: The Windsor-Essex County Health Unit, Essex County District Health Council.

30) Lopez, Alan, D. (1990) "Competing Causes of Death: A Review of Recent Trends in Mortality in Sixteen Industrialized Countries With Special Reference to Cancer" in *Trends in Cancer Mortality in Industrial Countries*, Derra Lee Davis & David Hoel (eds), New York: New York Academy of Sciences.

31) Mirer, Frank (1995) "Mortality Studies in UAW Represented Machining Plants" a paper presented at the *Machining Fluids Conference*, Dearborn, Michigan: November 1995.

32) *Report to the Workers' Compensation Board on the Health Effects of Occupational Exposure to Petroleum-based Fluids used for Making and Lubricating Metal in Manufacturing* (1995) Toronto: Occupational Disease Panel.

33) Eisen, Ellen A., Tolbert, Paige E., Monson, Richard R. & Smith, Thomas, J. (1992) "Mortality Studies of Machining Fluid Exposure in the Automobile Industry I: A Standardized Mortality Ratio Analysis" *American Journal of Industrial Medicine*, 22: 809-824.

34) Eisen, Ellen A., Tolbert, Paige, E., Hallock, Marilyn F., Monson, Richard R., Smith, Thomas J. & Woskie, Susan R. (1994) "Mortality Studies of Machining Fluid Exposure in the Automobile Industry III: A Case Control Study of Larynx Cancer" *American Journal of Industrial Medicine*, 26: 185-202.

35) *Report to the Workers' Compensation Board on Cardiovascular Disease and*

Cancer among Firefighters (1994) Toronto: Industrial Disease Standards Panel.

36)   Milkovic-Kraus, Sanja & Horvat, Durda   (1991)   "Chromosomal Abnormalities Among Nurses Occupationally Exposed to Antineoplastic Drugs" in *American Journal of Industrial Medicine*, Vol. 19, No. 6: 771- 774.

37)   Partanen, Timo & Boffetta, Paolo   (1994)   "Cancer Risk in Asphalt Workers and Roofers: Review and Meta-Analysis of Epidemiologic Studies" in *American Journal of Industrial Medicine*, Vol. 26, No. 6: 721-740.

38)   Blair, A., Linos, A., Stewart, P., Burmeister, L., Gibson, R., Everett, G., Schuman, L. & Cantor, K.   (1993)   "Evaluation of Risks for Non-Hodgkins Lymphoma by Occupation and Industry Exposures From A Case-Control Study" in *American Journal of Industrial Medicine*, Vol. 23, No. 6: 301-312.

39)   *Recommendations for the Primary Prevention of Cancer*, A Report of the Ontario Task Force on the Primary Prevention of Cancer (Anthony B. Miller, Chairman), March 1995.

40)   Greene, G. & Ratner, V.   (1994)   "A Toxic Link to Breast Cancer?" *The Nation*, June 20, 1994.

INDEX

A

accidents   32
American Industrial Health Council   9
animal tests   18
anti-neoplastic drugs   42
asbestos   5, 6
asbestos workers   17
asbestosis   6

B

bacteria tests   18
Bendix   7
bioconcentration   53

C

cable splicers   23
cancer
  in Australia   38
  and auto industry   38-39, 48
  and blue collar workers   40-41
  death rates   31-38
  definition   7
  in developing countries   37, 54
  environmental   3, 8, 9, 13, 14, 17, 48, 53-56
  in France   38
  genetic   8, 13
  in Hungary   38
  in Italy   38
  in Japan   38
  multifactorial   14
  in Netherlands   38
  occupational   4, 5, 8, 9, 14-16, 40, 43, 47, 49, 50-54
  in United Kingdom   38

The Authors:

Matthew Firth is a researcher/technical writer with the Windsor Occupational Health Information Service. He has a bachelor of Environmental Studies degree from the University of Waterloo and a Master of Arts degree from Queen's University (Kingston).

James Brophy is the Executive Director of Occupational Health Clinics for Ontario Workers - Windsor and a member of the Ontario Occupational Disease Panel. He is also a Senior Visiting Research Fellow at De Montfort University in England where he is enrolled in the PhD programme.

Margaret Keith is the Executive Director of the Windsor Occupational Health Information Service in Windsor, Ontario. She is also a Senior Visiting Research Fellow at De Montfort University in England, where she is enrolled in the M. Phil/PhD programme.